Tony B[...]

DEVON
QUIZ BOOK

*"Well blew me down – tha's
sommut I didn' knaw!"*

HALSGROVE

First published in Great Britain in 2009

Copyright © Tony Beard 2009
questions compiled by Jack Paynter © 2009

Cover Illustration by Charles Wood © 2009

British Library Cataloguing-in-Publication Data
A CIP record for this title is available from the British Library

ISBN 978 1 84114 934 9

HALSGROVE
Halsgrove House,
Ryelands Industrial Estate,
Bagley Road, Wellington, Somerset TA21 9PZ
Tel: 01823 653777   Fax: 01823 216796
email: sales@halsgrove.com

Part of the Halsgrove group of companies
Information on all Halsgrove titles is available at: www.halsgrove.com

Printed and bound by Short Run Press Limited

Introduction

by Tony Beard

I s'pose Jan Stewer might call this a 'parcel of old crams' but it is meant to be a light-hearted look at this wonderful county of Devon and what can be found around the odd corner, what you may hear about in the pub, or where you may feel like exploring just to learn more.

Here's a bit of fun that just may prompt you to venture out into 'The World of Wonder' that is Deb'm. Some of these questions may be very easy and some may make 'ee, scratch your 'ead, for a minute or two, and I hope some will make 'ee think long and hard for the answer.

The aim is have a bit of fun and to any 'Non-Devonian' into whose lap a copy of this book might fall or into whose stocking it appears on Christmas Morning, have a go at a little of our dialect. Try and unravel some of place-names and during the next year or so, try to visit some of the places mentioned and you will be thrilled at the history and heritage that you will find hidden away in the villages, towns and cities.

To the visitor to Deb'm enjoy the hospitality on offer here! And I do hope that you will appreciate the 'Diversity that is Devon', the coasts, the hills of Exmoor and Dartmoor, the lanes and scenery, the wildlife and the animals. Just one word of warning do not feed the Dartmoor Ponies. They can bite at one end and kick at the other; we want you to enjoy your visit and the Devonshire Experience, not suffer from it.

I hope by the time you get to the end of this book that you will have had fun and learnt a thing or two along the way.

If this has given you some ideas on which you may wish to expand your knowledge of Devon, so much the better.

Remember! Life is for Living. Do not take it too seriously. That way you will Live, Love and Laugh for longer, and that can't be a bad thing!

Tony Beard
Widecombe-in-the-Moor 2009

Warm-Up Round

1. What's the difference between a 'drishel' and a 'dashel' ?

2. Where is the 'Spanish Barn'?

3. Black swans are associated with which Devon town?

4. What is a native of Barnstaple called?

5. Which Exe-side village is famed for its Marine life?

6. If the Great Western is a railway, what is the Grand Western?

7. Where would you commonly find the Latin inscription *Auxilio Divinio*?

8. Budleigh Salterton lies at the mouth of which river?

9. At which sport would a Devon Dumpling be involved?

10. Where would you find Drake's Drum?

Answers on page 64.

Around the Villages

1. A Dartmoor village with 16 letters in its name?

2. Where is this well known Devon landmark?

3. Which Devon placename is derived from a literary work?

4. Famous artist Sir Joshua Reynolds was born here.

5. Name four villages whose names start with the word 'Wool'?

6. Scene of a disastrous flood in North Devon in 1952?

7. A South Devon fishing village washed away in a storm in 1917?

8. Little - , and Great - . Two villages lie close to each other. Complete their name.

9. Home of Devon's thriving Benedictine monastery.

10. Sounds like a pint-sized fishing village in East Devon?

11. A Stannary 'town' beginning with 'P'?

12. Where is it that England's highest waterfall is said to be found in Devon?

13. The last castle to be built in England stands near which village?

14. This fruit was originally grown in orchards at Dittisham on the River Dart, and takes its name from the village. What is it?

15. A Devon placename that means 'The water cress spring belonging to the King.' Where is it?

16. A railway halt and a famous area of sand dunes near the mouth of the Exe?

17. Name two Devon villages beginning with the letter 'Z'

18. In which village are donkey rides a common means of transport?

19. The largest surviving mill in Ivybridge makes what?

20. In which village is 'the Cathedral of North Devon'?

Answers on page 66.

Picture Poser 1

In January 2007 this ship was wrecked off the coast of Devon and thousands flocked to the beach where much of her cargo had been washed ashore. Name the ship.

Dialect Delights

1. What would a Devon farmworker do with a Bulhaggle?

2. What colours would an Appledrain be?

3. Who wrote the book *A Parcel of Ol' Crams*, written in Devon Dialect?

4. What kind of flower is a Goo'coo?

5. Where would you find a cloam egg?

6. If a fuzz pig is a hedgehog, what is a chuggypig?

7. What kind of bird is known as a Dish-washer?

8. You wouldn't want one of these in your garden. But what is a want?

9. What is the local dialect name for guinea fowl?

10. What kind of bird is a harnzee?

11. Not Popeye's girlfriend. What in Devonshire dialect is a goyle?

12. Cowflops and floppydocks describe which kind of flower?

13. Where would you find Grannie's Bonnet?

14. What is a moot?

15. Urts are what?

16. Yorks or Yarks or what?

17. What would you do with your croust?

18. Where would you find a linhay?

19. What colour is an ood-all?

20. Sabine Baring Gould collected stories and songs throughout Devon. One of his sources was Sally Satterly who lived at Jolly Lane Cot. Where is it? *Pictured.*

Answers on pages 66/67.

Picture Poser 2

Said to be one of the oldest continuously running annual regatta's in Britain, known to have taken place since at least 1817. Where is it?

Local Literature

1. Which famous author rented a farmhouse near Manaton on Dartmoor, from where he wrote his best-known trilogy *The Forsyte Saga*?

2. Who wrote *Life in a Devon Village*, and *Tales of a Devon Village* first published in 1945?

3. First published in serial form in 1901 and set on Dartmoor this became one of the most famous crime/mystery stories of all time.

4. Name the South Devon coastal resort where in 1818 John Keats wrote his famous poem *Endymion.*

5. This famous Reverend wrote the hymn 'Onward Christian Soldiers'. Who is he?

6. Burgh Island will forever be associated with the work of this famous crime novelist. Who is she?

7. Born in India where many of his stories are set, this writer went to school in North Devon. Name him.

8. Also born in India. His first name sounds like Heaven. He wrote many novels set on Dartmoor. Who is he?

9. Name the writer born at Holne in 1819, his most famous book is *The Water Babies*?

10. Born in Ottery St Mary he wrote *The Rime of the Ancient Mariner.*

11. Charles Dickens is one of the giants of English literature. His 'Fat Boy' is said to have been inspired by a character at the Turks Head Inn in the city. In which novel does he appear?

12. Who wrote the poem 'Drakes' Drum' which has the line 'Drake he was a Devon man and ruled the Devon seas'?

13. Jane Austen's *Sense and Sensibility* was

filmed partly in Devon in 1995. Which National Trust property features as 'Norland Park'.

14. Which author of a famous Guide to Dartmoor is buried in Mary Tavy churchyard?

15. Published in 1982, complete the title of this popular children's novel, written by Brian Carter: *A Black Fox* -------?

Answers on page 67.

An aerial view of which Devon resort?

Personality Parade

1. Which famous rabbit once 'hosted' his own show on local television?

2. Which member of the Rolling Stones band owns a stud farm in Devon?

3. World famous Devon-based artist best known for her paintings of larger-than-life women.

4. Devonport born, he is one of the best known of the 'Cambridge Five' spy ring?

5. Plymouth born Labour MP, he broke away to help found the Social Democratic Party.

6. Young Olympic diver specialising in the 10m platform event. Born and raised in Devon.

7. A Devonian and most infamous of all Royal Navy captains. Made a remarkable sea voyage when cast adrift by mutineers.

8. Paignton-born professional tennis player who is now best known as a TV presenter.

9. Explorer whose life ended in tragic but heroic circumstance. He was born in Devonport in 1868 and died in Antarctica in 1912.

10. Born in Torquay and one of a famous comedy duo. Founder also of *Private Eye*. Name him.

Answers on page 69.

Pews and Preachers

1. Devon Parson who gave his name to a breed of dog?

2. Exeter Cathedral contains one of the largest bells in England. What is its name?

3. Used as a gunpowder store during the Civil War this North Devon church blew up in 1646. Where is it?

4. When the villagers of Sampford Courtenay marched on Exeter in 1549 they sparked the beginning of what uprising?

5. The Bible Christian Society first met in this Devon village in 1815. Where?

6. Which church is known as the Cathedral of the Moor?

7. Which village church clock bears the text "My Dear Mother" instead of numerals?

8. Before Exeter became the seat of Devon's bishops in 1050, the centre of religion was in which Devon town.

9. Name the tiny chapel, near Dunkeswell, dedicated to Devon-raised John Graves Simcoe who became the first Lt Governor General of Upper Canada in 1791.

10. Born in the vicarage of Charles Church, Plymouth, the photograph below shows one of the Westcountry's great eccentric clergymen. Who is he?

Answers on page 69.

Half hidden by summer foliage the church tower of St Giles and St Nicholas stands in the midst of this fashionable South Devon resort. Where is it?

'appy anagrams

Unravel the names of these Devon towns & villages (some may be more than one word)

1. Dwarfish Wooly Tor

2. Token Stinging

3. Ape Hot Monk

4. A Renamed Moth Stop

5. Hell Hot Match It

6. A Lethargic Loon

7. Ferrets Renown

8. High Leather

9. Pry Beery Moor

10. Sent To

11. Huge Child

12. Oh Not In

13. Crept In Now

14. My rhubarb Ode

15. Remix Ants

16. Odd Brief

17. Posh Mat

18. Not A Shrub

19. No Taping

20. Lost Moon Hut

Answers on page 70.

This Sporting Life

1. Which Devon football team plays at Home Park?

2. Name the two premier horse racing courses in Devon.

3. The name of the Speedway team who formerly raced at Exeter's County Ground?

4. The team name of Exeter Rugby Club?

5. Where is the oldest golf course in the country?

6. In what sport did the contestants wear baked boots?

7. What are the colours of Exeter City Football Club's home strip.

8. Where is the North Devon Surf School located?

9. Gig Racing is popular in many Devon seaside towns. For what were gigs originally used?

10. Which Devon Cricket team plays at the ground seen in the photograph?

Answers on page 70/71.

The most southerly point in Devon. Where is it?

City Life: Exeter

1. Exeter Cathedral is dedicated to which Saint?

2. Name Exeter's two principal railway stations.

3. What did the Romans call the city of Exeter?

4. Southernhay, Princesshay, Northernhay and Friernhay are parts of the city. What is the origin of the word 'hay'?

5. The author of the Harry Potter books attended Exeter University. Who is she?

6. What was the original purpose for Exeter's famous Underground Passages?

7. The Exeter Blitz in 1942 was part of a series of raids on British cities ordered by Adolf Hitler. By what name were they known?

8. Name Exeter's Norman castle?

9. What is the length of the River Exe from source to sea?

10. Name the church in the photograph?

Answers on page 71.

City Life: Plymouth

1. The Pilgrim Fathers sailed from the Barbican (Mayflower Steps) in which year?

2. Plymouth Citadel is home base for which military force?

3. Smeaton's Tower stands on the Hoe, where was it originally sited?

4. Plymouth city now incorporates the original 'Three Towns', name the other two.

5. Which famous seaman by tradition is said to have played bowls on the Hoe, and when?

6. Name the railway bridge that connects Plymouth and Saltash.

7. Name two Breton ports to which ferries from Plymouth regularly sail.

8. Name Plymouth's four principal rivers.

9. Name the island that sits in Plymouth Sound.

10. Identify the three features marked A, B, and C in the photograph?

Answers on pages 71/72.

The highest Inn in Southern England at 1425 feet above sea level, and said to have had a fire burning in the hearth continuously since 1845.

Where is it?

What is the Inn called?

North Devon

1. Name the heroine in R.D. Blackmore's novel set on Exmoor.

2. Famous twentieth century Barnstaple-born mariner who was the first to sail single handed around the world?

3. North Devon's most famous member of the *Lutrinae* family?

4. Name the award-winning theatre in Ilfracombe.

5. North and South Molton are named after which river?

6. Sir Walter Raleigh is said to have landed the first ever shipment of tobacco at this North Devon port. Where is it?

7. Name the town at the mouth of the River Torridge, famed for its shipbuilding .

8. Playwright, poet and satirist, Barnstaple-born John Gay is most famous for which masterpiece?

9. One of the largest areas of sand dunes in Britain, home to 400 species of wildflowers. What is it called?

10. The highest point on the North Devon coast?

Answers on page 72.

East Devon

1. Famed as a mariner and explorer, this Woodbury-born navigator was the first to bring potatoes into Britain.

2. The Seaton Tramway runs from Seaton to where?

3. An East Devon town famous for carpet making. Name it.

4. In which East Devon town is 'Lace Walk' to be found?

5. Which Second World War airfield, five miles from Honiton, was used by the United States Navy from 1943.

6. Which East Devon coastal resort takes part of its name from the salt pans that were used to make salt for preserving.

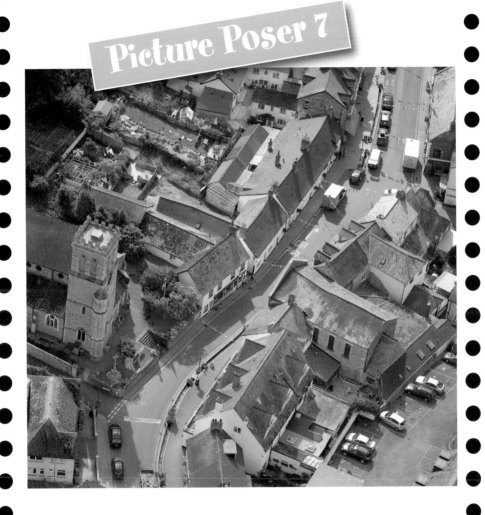

Sounds like a good place to quench your thirst.
But where is it?

Name this East Devon town.

7. This small River Sid gives its name to three settlements along its length. Name them.

8. A World Heritage Site named after a geological period, what is it called?

9. Lord Nelson's estranged wife and Lady Byron were among many rich and famous who came to live in this fashionable watering place. Name it.

10. Taking its name from the nearby East Devon town, this stone was used in the building of Exeter Cathedral. What is it called?

Answers on page 72.

West Devon

1. Site of an infamous castle dungeon and a Royal mint of King Ethelred. Where is it?

2. Opened in 1941 near Yelverton, this RAF base's name was changed in order not to be confused with Yeovilton airfield. What name did it take?

3. One of two Devon places with the same name. This village near Plymouth is the home of 42 Commando Royal Marines. Its name?

4. One of Devon's four stannary towns, and site of an ancient Abbey.

5. Terminus of the Tavistock canal and once a major port. Where is this heritage museum?

6. An Abbey, former home of Francis Drake.

Picture Poser 8

Name of this West Devon mine ruin?

7. Part of Dartmoor National Park but heavily mined for china clay. What is the area called?

8. Home to the Dartmoor Wildlife Park. Sounds like a bright place to be.

9. Bere Ferrers sits beside which river?

10. Said to be the village where Old Mother Hubbard's cottage once stood, giving rise to the nursery rhyme.

> *Old Mother Hubbard*
> *Went to the cupboard,*
> *To give the poor dog a bone:*
> *When she came there,*
> *The cupboard was bare,*
> *And so the poor dog had none.*

Answers on page 73.

South Devon

1. Part of this area is known as the South Hams. What is a 'Ham' in this context?

2. The largest natural freshwater lake in southern England sits behind a shingle ridge protected from the sea. Name it.

3. Totnes sits at the head of which river estuary?

4. When was Britannia Royal Naval College opened?

5. Name the three main towns that make up the civil district known as Torbay.

6. A well known cut-price shopping centre near Newton Abbot that takes its name from its Cornish counterpart?

7. The nickname of Torquay United Football Club?

8. Name the first town in Britain to elect a member of the Official Monster Raving Loony Party to public office.

9. What was the original name of Newton Abbot?

10. This clock in the photo below stands above which South Devon town?

Answers on page 73.

Dartmoor

1. When was Dartmoor first designated as a National Park?

2. It's name means 'High'. What is this best known of all Dartmoor Tors called?

3. Webbers and Bowdens are two stores whose popularity spreads far beyond the borders of this Dartmoor town. Where are they to be found?

4. What are the Nine Maidens and where can they be found?

5. The southernmost of Dartmoor's reservoirs lies behind this dam. It's name?

6. The High Moorland Visitor Centre is located where?

7. Dartmoor's most prominent Nose? Name it.

8. Home of one of Britain's most famous annual fairs, celebrated in song. Where is it and when is it held?

Picture Poser 9

A typical Dartmoor clapper bridge. But which?

Name the place where it can be found.

9. A famous legend is associated with this grave, said always to be decorated with freshly picked flowers. Name it.

10. Can you identify the place shown in the photograph below and say for what purpose it was originally built?

Answers on page 74.

Cryptic Communities

(Can you identify these places?)

1. Sooty residue at the Gents' Outfitters.

2. She broke down after the wedding.

3. Having jolly fun in this Dartmoor valley.

4. Sounds like you get the perfect reception in the North Devon village.

5. Soaking the woolly beasts.

6. A hive of religious bees.

7. Tied up neatly.

8. Get together for a pub game.

9. What the Count's wife dresses in.

10. Building up the archangel's fire.

11. Just the place to buy a bar of chocolate.

This Crediton-born soldier became a General and VC holder. Who is he and where is this statue?

12. Where the rodents are kept.

13. Not outgoing - just the opposite.

14. Crown, ermine robes, it's what the monarch has on.

15. Between the trenches.

16. A cry to get the wagons moving.

17. Utterly?

18. Weighty timber in Exeter suburb.

19 Celebrity in a bad mood.

20. Promontory where the spanner fits.

Answers on pages 74 and 76.

Anagrams Too

Unravel the names of Devon's towns & villages (some may be more than one word)

1. Hot Lumpy

2. Begin Sin Hotspot

3. Pick The Salt.

4. Tin Door Gong

5. Flick Huge Bats

6. Wash Lid

7. No Grating Retort

8. Nearest Bike

9. Select No Pop

10. Becalm So

11. Yes I Nag Her

12. Novel Tyre

13. Duck Once Hid

14. Sled Will Do

15. Wending Otters

16. Chunky Tea

17. Error By Barn

18. Stole Hunter

19. On Tours

20. Hid Girt Ewe

Answers on page 76.

Picture Poser 11

One of North Devon's most famous villages.

Can you name it?

Myths and Legends

1. Name the church built standing on a hill on western Dartmoor that was, according to legend, built by a merchant saved from shipwreck.

2. Jack Rattenbury of Beer has many stories written about a nefarious past. What was he famous for?

3. According to legend a death in the Oxenham family of Zeal Monachorum is foretold by the appearance of what creature?

4. This family were said to inhabit the wastes of Dartmoor preying on travellers in the 16th century. Their name?

5. What did the devil leave behind following a snowstorm in 1855?

6. This prominent rock formation off the coast near Dawlish forms part of a legend involving two churchmen. What is the name given to the rocks?

7. Local stories have it that more than one motorist has found themselves driven off the road at a spot between Princetown and Postbridge on Dartmoor. By what name is this legend known?

8. Name the manor house in North Devon said to be among the most haunted dwelling in Britain.

9. Name the waterfall in Lydford Gorge.

10. An ancient oak wood on Dartmoor said to be haunted by the Devil's hounds. Its name?

Answers on page 77.

This South Devon ruin is said to be haunted by a White Lady.

Can you name the castle?

Festivals and Events

1. Held on the 2nd Wednesday in October each year in Tavistock name this annual event.

2. This Ram Roast held in May each year is one of South Devon's most popular events. Where is it held?

3. The British Firework Championships are held here each year. Where?

4. The Devon County Show is held where and when?

5. Devon's premier annual May exhibition of art is held in galleries and grounds of this house in Cornwood. Its name?

6. Navy Days are held in September simultaneously in two naval ports, Portsmouth is one, what is the other?

A burning tar barrel is carried through the streets on bonfire night.

Name the Devon town where this occurs.

7. Beautiful Days is a music festival held annually in August in East Devon. Name the venue.

8. May Day celebrations and the crowning of the May Queen are among Devon's best known annual events held in this small Dartmoor village. Its name?

9. Folk music is the central theme of this long-running annual festival held in an East Devon resort. Name the place.

10. Clovelly has a festival named after a fish. What fish and when is the festival held?

Answers on page 78.

Devon General Knowledge

1. The A38 trunk road between Exeter and Plymouth is also known as what?

2. Kirton is the old name given to which Devon town?

3. Where is the ancestral seat of the Dukes of Devonshire (not in Devon!)?

4. Which four creatures appear on the Devon Coat of Arms?

5. A name of an American car (last made in 2001) is also the name of a Devon place. Which?

6. Name the French town with which Exeter is twinned.

7. The Long Bridge has 24 arches. Where is it?

8. Not far from Torquay, this famous old forge is a major tourist attraction. Name it.

9. This long distance footpath traverses Devon from Ivybridge to Lynton. It's name?

10. If Devon is famous for its cider, what alcoholic drink is Plymouth known for?

11. Name the Devon town, lying close to the Somerset border, famed for its Pony Fair held in October each year.

12. Dartmoor's greatest challenge for walkers. Name this annual event.

13. Name the harbour where a replica of Sir Francis Drake's *Golden Hind* is permanently on show.

14. Born in Kingsbridge he was famous for the discovery of China Clay in Britain and his development of English porcelain. His name?

15. Name the Arts Centre in Great Torrington which takes its name from a former public house.

16. The headquarters of the Dartmoor National Park are to be found in this National Trust-owned property. Name it.

Picture Poser 14

By no means an ordinary railway. This one works on water power.

Where is it?

17. Based in Plymouth, name the region's largest selling daily newspaper.

18. A charitable emergency helicopter service run for the benefit of local people. What is its official title?

19. 'The Mad Axeman' was one of Dartmoor Prison's most notorious inmates. What was his real name?

20. If the Red Devon is a famous breed of cattle, what kind of creature is the Devonshire Red?

Answers on pages 78 and 80.

Tony Beard's
DEVON
QUIZ BOOK
ANSWERS

PICTURE POSERS ANSWERS

Picture Poser 1 The *Napoli*.

Picture Poser 2 Shaldon Regatta take place annually in August.

Picture Poser 3 Dawlish, South Devon.

Picture Poser 4 Sidmouth Parish Church

Picture Poser 5 Start Point

Picture Poser 6 The Warren House Inn between Postbridge and Moretonhampstead on Dartmoor.

Picture Poser 7 Fore Street, Beer.

Picture Poser 8 Wheal Betsy Engine House, north of Mary Tavy.

Picture Poser 9 Postbridge

Picture Poser 10 General Sir Henry Redvers Buller (1839-1908). The statue stands in Exeter at the junction of New North Road and Queen Street.

Picture Poser 11 Clovelly.

Picture Poser 12 Berry Pomeroy Castle. The White Lady is said to haunt the dungeons, and rises from St Margaret's Tower to the castle ramparts. According to legend she is the spirit of Margaret Pomeroy, who was imprisoned in the dungeons by her jealous sister Eleanor.

Picture Poser 13 Ottery St Mary.

Picture Poser 14 Lynton and Lynmouth Cliff Railway, North Devon.

Picture Poser 15 At Brixham where William and his army first landed.

Picture Poser 16 Powderham.

Picture Poser 17 Tiverton.

Picture Poser 18 Blackpool Sands, South Devon.

WARM-UP ROUND ANSWERS

1. In Devon dialect a drishel is a thrush, a dashel is a thistle.
2. Torquay. It's the name given to the Tithe Barn at Torre Abbey.
3. Dawlish.
4. Barumites - after 'Barum' the original name of the town.
5. Lympstone - principal training centre for the Royal Marines.
6. The canal that was originally built to run between Tiverton and Taunton.
7. On the Devon County coat of arms - 'By Divine Aid'.
8. The River Otter.
9. Cricket. It's the name of one of the county's oldest clubs, founded in 1902.
10. At Buckland Abbey - Buckland Monachorum.

William of Orange landed in Devon in 1688 to reclaim the throne from King James II. Where is this statue to be found?

AROUND THE VILLAGES ANSWERS

1. Moretonhampstead.
2. On Haldon Hill. It's Haldon Belvedere.
3. Westward Ho!
4. Plympton St Maurice.
5. There are many, including: Woolfardisworthy, Woolsery (Woolfardisworthy), Woolacombe, Wooladon, Woolbrok, Woolcombe, Woolfin, Woolhanger, Woolladon, Woollaton, Woolleigh, Woolley, Woolridge, Woolsgrove, Woolwell.
6. Lynmouth.
7. Hallsands.
8. Torrington.
9. Buckfast.
10. Beer.
11. Plympton
12. Canonteign (220 feet), near Christow
13. Drewsteignton (Castle Drogo).
14. Dittisham plum.
15. Kingskerswell.
16. Dawlish Warren.
17. There are 4: Zeal, Zeal Monachorum, Zeaston and Zempson.
18. Clovelly.
19. Paper.
20. Stoke, near Hartland.

DIALECT DELIGHTS ANSWERS

1. Set it up in a field. It's a scarecrow. Also known as a 'mommet'.
2. Yellow and black - it's a wasp.
3. Jan Stewer (Albert J. Coles 1876-1965)
4. A bluebell. Possibly as they come into bloom at the same time as the Cuckoo can be heard. Lady's Smock (*Cardamine pratensis*) or Milkmaid is also sometimes known as the Cuckoo flower.
5. In a chicken coop. Ceramic or clay eggs were used to encourage chickens to lay.
6. A woodlouse.
7. The pied wagtail.

8. A mole.

9. Gleanies (also known as 'chop-ats' because of their call).

10. A heron.

11. A steep cut into a hillside. A gully - often associated with mining.

12. Foxgloves.

13. In the garden or hedgerow. It's the folk-name of Columbine.

14. A tree stump.

15. Whortleberries.

16. String or straps tied below the knee to keep trousers out of the mud, and to stop things running up your trouser leg!

17. Eat it. It's the name for dinner (lunch), usually eaten in the open air.

18. In a farmyard or field. It's an open-sided barn.

19. Either black and white or green. It's a woodpecker.

20. Hexworthy, on Dartmoor.

LOCAL LITERATURE ANSWERS

1. John Galsworthy.

2. Henry Williamson, author of *Tarka the Otter*.

3. *The Hound of the Baskervilles* by Arthur Conan Doyle. The famous Grimpen Mire in which the evil Jack Stapleton is drowned is said to have been inspired by Fox Tor mire.

4. John Keats stayed in Teignmouth. There's a plaque commemorating this in Northumberland Place.

5. Sabine Baring Gould (1834-1924). He was rector of Lew Trenchard.

6. Agatha Christie, who lived at Greenway overlooking the Dart, spent holidays at Burgh Island where she wrote some of her most famous stories.

7. Rudyard Kipling was educated at Westward Ho!.

8. Eden Phillpotts (1862-1960) wrote, among other books, *Widecombe Fair*.

9. Charles Kingsley (1819-1875).

10. Samuel Taylor Coleridge (1772-1834).

11. *The Pickwick Papers*.

12. Henry Newbolt.

13. Saltram House.

14. William Crossing (1847-1928)

15. *A Black Fox Running*.

Picture Poser 16

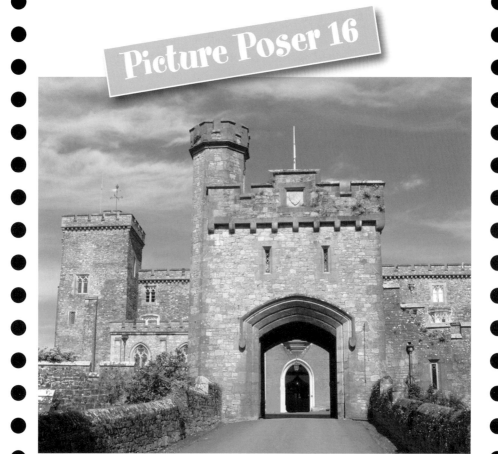

The gatehouse to one of Devon's finest castles. It is the home of the Courtenay family and overlooks the River Exe.

What is the castle called?

PERSONALITY PARADE ANSWERS

1. Gus Honeybun. A puppet that featured on Westward and later TSW from 1961 until 1992.
2. Charlie Watts (the drummer).
3. Beryl Cook (1937-2008)
4. Guy Francis De Moncy Burgess was born in Albemarle Villas, Devonport in 1911.
5. David Owen.
6. Tom Daley.
7. Captain William Bligh (1754-1817), of *Bounty* fame..
8. Sue Barker.
9. Robert Falcon Scott (Scott of the Antarctic).
10. Peter Cook (1937-1995).

PEWS AND PREACHERS ANSWERS

1. Rev Jack Russell is said to have been the original breeder of the terriers named after him.
2. 'Great Peter'. It weighs in at 80cwt.
3. Torrington was one of the last battles of the English Civil War in February 1646. The church was used both as a prison and a gunpowder store when suddenly there was a massive explosion destroying the church and much of the town and killing the 200 prisoners within.
4. The Western Rising or Prayer Book Rebellion. The parishioners had compelled their priest to revert to the old prayer book after the Act of Uniformity made it illegal to use the old Latin prayer book.
5. Shebbear.
6. St Pancras Church, Widecombe-in-the-Moor.
7. St Peter's Church Buckland-in-the-Moor. The clock was donated by William Whitley in 1931 in memory of his mother.
8. Crediton.
9. Wolford Chapel.
10. Rev Robert Stephen Hawker.

'APPY ANAGRAMS ANSWERS

1. Woolfardisworthy
2. Kingsteignton
3. Okehampton
4. Moretonhampstead
5. Chittlehamholt
6. Colaton Raleigh
7. Newton Ferrers
8. Hatherleigh
9. Berry Pomeroy
10. Totnes
11. Chudleigh
12. Honiton
13. Princetown
14. Broadhembury
15. Axminster
16. Bideford
17. Topsham
18. Ashburton
19. Paignton
20. South Molton

THIS SPORTING LIFE ANSWERS

1. Plymouth Argyle FC.
2. Exeter Race Course (Haldon) and Newton Abbot Race Course.
3. The Exeter Falcons.
4. The Chiefs.
5. The Royal North Devon Golf Club claims to have the oldest course in England, founded in 1864.
6. Devon wrestling. Popular in the nineteenth century the participants would concentrate on kicking the shins of their opponent.

7. Red and white.
8. Westward Ho!
9. In the late 17th century gigs were working boats in the South West, ferrying pilots out to incoming vessels to help them navigate through the rocks and safely into harbour.
10. Sidmouth Cricket Club.

CITY LIFE: EXETER ANSWERS

1. St Peter.
2. Exeter St David's and Exeter Central.
3. Isca (Dumnoniorum).
4. A 'hay' is a piece of land or field enclosed by a hedge.
5. J.K. Rowling
6. Begun in the 14th century, they were conduits for bringing fresh water into the city.
7. The were known as the Baedeker Raids, so called as Hitler was said to have referred to this early tourist guide to pick out cities of historic note, rather than purely military targets.
8. Rougemont Castle.
9. 50 miles.
10. St Michael and All Angels.

CITY LIFE: PLYMOUTH ANSWERS

1. 1620.
2. The Royal Marine Commandos (29 Commando Regiment Royal Artillery).
3. On the Eddystone Rocks. It was the third lighthouse to be built there.
4. Devonport and East Stonehouse.
5. Sir Francis Drake, in 1588.

6. The Royal Albert Bridge, completed in 1859.
7. St Malo and Roscoff.
8. Tamar, Lynher, Plym and Tavy.
9. Drake's Island.
10. A The Lido. B The Civic Centre. C Smeaton's Tower.

NORTH DEVON ANSWERS

1. Lorna Doone (from the novel of the same name).
2. Sir Francis Chichester
3. Tarka (it's the Latin name for otter)
4. The Landmark Theatre.
5. The River Mole
6. Bideford.
7. Appledore
8. *The Beggars Opera*, first performed in 1728.
9. Braunton Burrows.
10. Great Hangman.

EAST DEVON ANSWERS

1. Sir Walter Raleigh.
2. Colyton.
3. Axminster.
4. Honiton. A town once famed for its lace making.
5. Dunkeswell
6. Budleigh Salterton.
7. Sidmouth, Sidford and Sidbury.
8. The Jurassic Coast.
9. Exmouth.
10. Beer Stone.

WEST DEVON ANSWERS

1. Lydford.
2. RAF Harrowbeer.
3. Bickleigh.
4. Tavistock.
5. Morwellham Quay
6. Buckland Abbey.
7. Lee Moor.
8. Sparkwell.
9. River Tavy.
10. Yealmpton.

SOUTH DEVON ANSWERS

1. It means 'an enclosed or sheltered place' - from the Old English 'Hamme' .
2. Slapton Ley.
3. The River Dart.
4. 1905. Before that date naval officers were trained on a wooden hulk HMS *Britannia* moored in the River Dart
5. Brixham, Paignton and Torquay.
6. Trago Mills.
7. The Gulls.
8. Ashburton. Local publican Alan Hope was first elected to Ashburton Town Council in 1989. He later became Mayor of the town.
9. Newton Bushel was the original settlement. The Bushel family were the major landowners in the area. It later merged with Newton Abbot and took on that name in 1633.
10. Kingsbridge.

DARTMOOR ANSWERS

1. 1951.
2. Haytor. It's the most visited of all Dartmoor tors.
3. In Chagford.
4. The Nine Maidens are a circle of stones that once formed the outer wall of a Bronze Age burial chamber. They can be found near Belstone.
5. The Avon Dam holds back the waters of the Avon Reservoir
6. At Princetown. It's the principal information centre of the Dartmoor National Park Authority.
7. Bowerman's Nose is a prominent and well-known geological feature standing on Hayne Down near Manaton. Many folk tales are associated with it.
8. Widecombe Fair, made famous in the song containing characters such as Tom Pearse, Uncle Tom Cobley and Jan Stewer, is held annually on the second Tuesday in September at Widecombe-in-the-Moor.
9. Jay's Grave, near Hound Tor, is said to be the last resting place of Kitty Jay who took her own life when jilted by her lover.
10. HM Prison, Princetown. It was originally built to house Napoleonic prisoners of war.

CRYPTIC COMMUNITIES ANSWERS

1. Ashburton.
2. Bridestowe
3. Merrivale.
4. Welcombe.
5. Sheepwash.
6. Honeychurch.
7. Bow.
8. Dartmeet.
9. Countess Wear.
10. Stoke Gabriel.
11. Cadbury.
12. Rattery.
13. Inwardleigh.
14. Kingswear.

Blundells old school was opened in 1604 under the benefaction of a local merchant.
In which Devon town is it to be found?

15   Nomansland.

16   Westward Ho!

17. Butterleigh.

18. Heavitree.

19. Starcross.

20. Bolt Head.

ANAGRAMS TOO ANSWERS

1. Plymouth.
2. Bishopsteignton.
3. Sticklepath.
4. Goodrington.
5. Buckfastleigh.
6. Dawlish.
7. Great Torrington.
8. Kentisbeare.
9. Copplestone.
10. Salcombe.
11. Ashreigney.
12. Yelverton.
13. Dunchideock.
14. Loddiswell.
15. Drewsteignton.
16. Tuckenhay.
17. Berrynarbor.
18. Thurlestone.
19. Sourton.
20. Witheridge.

MYTHS AND LEGENDS ANSWERS

1. St Michael's church, Brent Tor. According to legend the church was built by a wealthy merchant whose ship was caught in a violent storm. Fearing that the ship would capsize, he prayed to God that if he were saved he would build a church on the first piece of land that he saw.

2. Smuggling. Jack Rattenbury is famous not only because he was a smuggler but because he wrote a diary of his activities and then published it.

3. A white bird. Some stories say it is a dove, others that the bird is a thrush or a ring ouzel

4. Gubbins. In the sixteenth century this notorious gang of outlaws lived near Lydford. They were led by one Roger Rowle and were the scourge of the area, notorious for stealing sheep on the moor.

5. A mysterious trail known as The Devil's Footprints. These appeared overnight in heavy snowfall in Southern Devon in 1855. According to contemporary reports, they stretched for over a hundred miles, and went over buildings, high walls and haystacks, appearing on the other side as though there was no barrier. They have never been adequately explained.

6. The Parson and Clerk. Now under threat from the erosion. Legend has it that a certain priest had to make frequent journeys to Dawlish, where the Bishop of Exeter lay ill. His clerk usually made a competent guide, but one night they lost their way. Angrily the priest remarked that the Devil would make a better guide. Just then a figure appeared and led the way to a brightly lighted house, where the parson and the clerk drank and ate amongst a strange looking company. But in the morning, before either man had time to ride away, the house disappeared, and both were drowned by the inrushing sea.

7. The Hairy Hands. According to the story a pair of disembodied hands appear suddenly, grab at the steering wheel of a moving car or the handlebars of a motorcycle, and then force the victim off the road.

8. Chambercombe Manor, near Ilfracombe. Female skeletal remains were found here in 1865, said to be a lady who was found shipwrecked on nearby rocks. The bones were sealed in a room. Her footsteps are heard walking along corridors, and a low moaning has been heard coming from the former secret room where her remains were found.

9. The White Lady waterfall. Legend has it that the source of the name of the waterfall is that anyone who falls into the Lyd and sees the figure of a woman in white with long flowing tresses standing in the waterfall will not drown.

10. Wistman's Wood. It is said to takes it's name from the word 'Wisht' which has associations with the supernatural, in this case the wisht hounds are said to belong to the devil.

FESTIVALS AND EVENTS ANSWERS

1. The Goose Fair. Held in Tavistock it dates back to the early 12th century, when a Michaelmas Fair provided the opportunity for business and animal trading. The name Goose Fair probably came about as farmers brought their geese ready for fattening for Christmas, and the only other Goose Fair (in Nottingham) has a similar connection.
2. Kingsteignton. Every year in May the inhabitants roast a whole ram, continuing a long tradition. Some say the festival dates back to pre-Christian times.
3. Plymouth. The Hoe is crowded with onlookers as one of the biggest firework shows in Britain takes place out in Plymouth Sound.
4. The Devon County Show is held annually in May at the Westpoint, near Exeter.
5. Delamore. The public have a chance each year to visit the house and gardens to see an exhibition of art and sculpture.
6. Devonport, Plymouth. Though interrupted in recent years, this important event has seen a recent revival.
7. Escot Park, near Fairmile. Beautiful Days describes itself as a family music festival.
8. Lustleigh. The May Day celebrations are the biggest event of the year for the village, with a carnival procession, maypole dancing, and crowning of the May Queen. A granite boulder has inscribed upon it the names of all the May Queens.
9. Sidmouth. Now called Sidmouth Folkweek, it is held in the first week in August.
10. Clovelly's Herring Festival takes place in November. Described as one of the best autumnal food fairs in the UK, the day aims to promote sustainable fishing, to help safeguard the livelihoods of fishermen, and to support the local economy.

DEVON GENERAL KNOWLEDGE ANSWERS

1. The Devon Expressway.
2. Crediton.
3. Chatsworth House, Derbyshire.
4. A bull, a Dartmoor pony, a lion and a sea lion.
5. Plymouth.
6. Renne.
7. Bideford.

Sounding more likes it's famous Northern seaside namesake, this beach is among the most popular in South Devon.

Name the beach.

8. Cockington.
9. The Two Moors Way.
10. Plymouth Gin.
11. Bampton.
12. Ten Tors.
13. Brixham.
14. William Cookworthy.
15. The Plough.
16. Parke, near Bovey Tracey.
17. The *Western Morning News*.
18. The Devon Air Ambulance (Trust).
19. Frank Mitchell. He was an associate of the Kray Twins.
20. It's the name given to a breed of fowl (chicken).